Easy Questions for Young Listeners

by
Janet A. Miles

Illustrated by Tom Matthews

**Academic
Communication
Associates**

P.O. Box 4279
Oceanside, CA 92052-4279

Academic
Communication
Associates

P.O. Box 4279
Oceanside, California 92052-4279

Printed in the United States of America
International Standard Book Number: 1-57503-016-0

Table of Contents

Introduction

When providing services for young children with communication disorders, it is important to educate parents about the specific difficulties that the child is experiencing and to provide materials to help the child overcome these difficulties. The materials selected must be age-appropriate and must contain content relevant to the specific needs of the child.

This book can be used to help children overcome deficiencies in attention, listening comprehension, vocabulary, syntax/morphology, and oral expression as they respond to questions and perform activities related to the content of short stories. The activities also help parents ask questions to elicit language from their children. The activities are most appropriate for preschool and kindergarten-age children with a language age between 2.5 and 5 years.

With guidance from the speech-language pathologist or special education teacher, parents can administer the lessons in the home environment. As parents participate in the activities, they learn to use questioning strategies to facilitate comprehension, to expand vocabulary, and to improve children's functional use of language.

Each of the 30 stories in this book includes a line drawing, questions to ask the child about the story, language expansion activities, and a reproducible response form. The questions contained within the story target developmental syntax/morphological structures and basic concepts necessary for effective communication. A question follows each sentence in the short story. These questions can be presented during the reading of the story or after the entire story is read.

Presenting the Activities

The activities should be presented as follows:

1. Place the story picture in front of the child. Introduce the characters shown in this picture.

2. Read the story to the child. Ask the student to listen carefully to the story.

3. Read the story a second time, pausing following each sentence to ask the question listed in bold type. If the student demonstrates the attention skills necessary to listen to the entire story without distraction, the questions can be asked after the entire story has been read.

1

4. Ask the child to retell the story. Present prompts if necessary.

5. Present the language expansion activities that follow the story. Adapt these activities, if necessary, to make them relevant to the interests and experiences of the student.

Recording Responses

A reproducible response form is included for each of the 30 stories. This form includes space for recording answers to the story comprehension questions. Space is also provided for recording the child's retelling of the story.

The *Activity Skills Checklist* on page 3 can be used to record observations made during program implementation. This checklist is a listing of many of the skills emphasized within the instructional activities.

Language Expansion Activities

The language expansion activities require the student to answer questions and to follow directions related to the content of the short stories. These questions may be modified to make them appropriate for the specific needs of the student. Questions requiring a verbal response, for example, can be modified to require a pointing response if the student's verbal capabilities are limited.

Questions such as "Can you make one balloon red and another one blue?" are designed to elicit a "yes" or "no" response and the performance of an activity. Prompts should be provided if the child fails to perform the activity spontaneously.

When parents present the activities in this book, they are able to reinforce language skills taught in the classroom or in the speech-language intervention program. The parent letter on page 4 may be distributed to parents to give them an overview of the intervention process.

All of the worksheets in this volume may be reproduced for use in instructional programs. Parents should be encouraged to use the short stories in conjunction with other stories selected by the child. By learning to ask questions effectively, parents can help their child develop the language and thinking skills necessary for success in the classroom curriculum.

Easy Questions for Young Listeners   *Activity Skills Checklist*

Student:_____   Date:_____

Scoring: + = no problems observed   0 = problems observed

___Comprehension of "wh" question forms

___Comprehension of yes/no questions

___Comprehension of basic concepts
    ___size (e.g., big, small)
    ___number
    ___shape
    ___quantity
    ___loudness (loud, soft)

___Comprehension of *same* and *different*

___Follows simple verbal task instructions: (e.g., color, trace, point to)

___Recalls story details

___Sequences story details

___Labels nouns

___Names basic colors

___Names basic shapes (e.g., round, circle, square)

___Describes characteristics of nouns

___Describes actions/events

___Describes feelings

___Describes locations (e.g., inside, outside)

___Produces grammatical sentences
    ___Use of *is*
    ___Use of *are*
    ___Use of *ing* at end of verbs (e.g., eating)
    ___Use of prepositions
    ___Use of pronouns

Other concerns:

Letter to Parents

Student: _____   Date:_____

To: _____

From:_____

Dear Parent:

These activity pages can be used to help your child improve both listening and speaking skills. They can be used in a variety of ways.

1. If your child is using two and three word combinations, you should first read a sentence and immediately ask the corresponding question. If your child responds with only one word, please model a correct two or three word sentence. If your child imitates the sentence, offer praise by saying "good talking." If the child does not provide a correct response, reinforce him/her for good listening. If the child answers incorrectly, provide the correct word.

2. If your child is a good listener, read all of the sentences to make a short "story." Then ask your child to respond to the questions. If he can't remember the correct answer, re-read the appropriate sentence. Always model your child's response using correct grammar. You also may want to expand his or her verbal response.

If your child is not ready for coloring activities, turn the instruction into a "point to" task (example: "Point to the shoe.").

Have fun! Once you've experienced the "questioning" routine, try to add a few questions of your own to the activities!

Sincerely,

Instructional
Activities

Activity 1
Birthday Balloons

Danny is blowing up balloons.

What is Danny doing?

The balloons are for a party.

What are the balloons for?

It is Danny's birthday.

Whose birthday is it?

Danny will give a balloon to each of his friends.

What will Danny do with the balloons?

Language Expansion Activities

1. Danny is a little boy. Are you little or big?

2. Would you like to color Danny's clothes? Can you name what he is wearing?

3. His balloons are all different colors. Look at the balloon he is holding. Color it yellow.

4. The balloons are round. They make a circle. Can you trace one of the balloons with your crayon before you color it?

5. Can you make one balloon red and another one blue?

6. Can you count the balloons on the ground? Now count the balloons in the air. How many balloons do you see?

Story 1- Birthday Balloons

Activity 2
Mary's Picnic

Mary is going on a picnic.

Where is Mary going?

She is carrying a heavy basket.

What is heavy?

The basket is full of food.

What is in the basket?

Mary will eat the food for lunch.

Who will eat the food?

Language Expansion Activities

1. Point to something on Mary's head. Did you point to the hat? Color the hat red.

2. Baskets are brown. What color do you need to make the basket?

3. Is Mary holding the basket in one hand or two? How many hands do you have? Can you carry something in just one hand? What?

4. Is Mary outside or inside?

5. Use green to color the grass.

6. What is Mary wearing? What color would you like to make Mary's dress? Did you color the dress the same color as her hat or a different color?

Story 2- Mary's Picnic

Activity 3
Going Fishing

Johnny is going fishing.

Where is Johnny going?

He is carrying a pole in one hand.

What is Johnny carrying?

He is holding a worm in the other hand.

What is in his other hand?

Johnny fishes at a pond.

Where does Johnny fish?

Language Expansion Activities

1. Can you point to the pole in Johnny's hand? Do you remember what he is holding in the other hand?

2. The worm wiggles. Can you wiggle your finger like a worm? Color the worm pink?

3. Johnny has something on his head. What is it? Can you touch the hat?

4. Do you see Johnny's hair? Where is it?

5. Do you have a favorite hat? Color Johnny's hat the same color as your hat.

6. Johnny looks very happy. Can you give me a happy look? Do you think fishing is fun? What is Johnny going to catch?

Story 3- Going Fishing

Activity 4
Take My Picture

Polly has a new camera.

What does Polly have?

She is taking pictures.

What is Polly doing with the camera?

She wants to take your picture.

Whose picture does she want to take?

She will tell you, "Smile."

What will she tell you?

Language Expansion Activities

1. Do you have a camera? Who has one at your house? Most cameras are black. Can you color just the camera? Did you use black?

2. When you look in a camera, you close one eye. Touch Polly's closed eye. Can you close just one eye? Touch her other eye. Is it open or closed?

3. How many hands is Polly using to hold the camera? Can you count them?

4. She is wearing a sweater. What color do you want to color it? How about her pants? Will you color them the same color or a different color?

5. Look at Polly's hair. Is her hair long or short? Is your hair long or short? Is my hair long or short?

Story 4- Take My Picture

Activity 5
Let's Play Ball

Ben is playing baseball.

What is Ben doing?

Baseball is his favorite game.

What is his favorite game?

He is wearing a glove on one hand.

Where is the glove?

Ben is holding his glove up.

Is he holding the glove up or down?

He will catch the ball with the glove.

What will he do with the glove?

Language Expansion Activities

1. Find the ball in the picture. Is the ball round? Color the ball green.

2. Where is the baseball glove? Color it brown.

3. Do you ever play ball? Do you play ball inside or outside? Who plays with you? Is your ball big or little?

4. Ben's favorite baseball team is the Red Sox. Can you color his shirt and shorts red? What color do you want to make his socks?

Story 5- Let's Play Ball

Activity 6
A Special Toy

Katie is holding a toy bunny.

What is she holding?

Katie loves her bunny.

Does Katie love her bunny?

The bunny's name is Floppy.

What is the bunny's name?

Floppy sleeps with Katie at night.

Who sleeps with Floppy?

Language Expansion Activities

1. Do you have a special toy? What is it?

2. You can color Floppy your favorite color. What color did you pick?

3. Look at Katie's face. Does she look happy or sad?

4. She is giving Floppy a hug. Will that make her feel better?

5. Katie needs a color on her hair. Why not make her hair the same color as yours? What color did you use?

Story 6- A Special Toy

Activity 7
Butterflies

Andy is standing very still.

Is Andy standing or sitting?

He is watching the butterflies.

What is he watching?

The butterflies are flying around Andy.

Where are the butterflies flying?

When Andy moves, the butterflies will fly away.

What will happen when Andy moves?

Andy will try to catch the butterflies in his net.

What will Andy try to catch in his net?

Language Expansion Activities

1. Pick three colors. What colors did you pick?

2. Color each butterfly a different color. Can you count the butterflies?

3. What color do you want to make Andy's hat? Color it now.

4. He is wearing a red shirt. What color will you color the shirt?

5. Andy is wearing glasses. Tell me about his glasses.

Story 7- Butterflies

Activity 8
Work of Art

Jill likes to paint.

What does Jill like to do?

She is holding her paint brush.

What is she holding in her hand?

She is painting on the paper.

Where is she painting?

She painted a picture of one house.

How many pictures did she paint?

She is going to give the picture to her mom.

Who is she going to give the picture to?

Language Expansion Activities

1. Can you find the paint jars. How many do you see? Color each jar a different color. What colors did you pick?

2. How many flowers did Jill paint? What colors would you like to make the flowers? Will you color them all the same color or different colors?

3. What did Jill paint? Can you name the parts of the house? (window, door, roof, etc.) What do you see in the sky?

4. Does Jill look happy or sad? Do you think her mom will be surprised?

Story 8- Work of Art

Activity 9
Halloween Night

Molly is going to her friend's party on Halloween.

Where is Molly going?

She is dressed in her Halloween costume.

What is she wearing?

Her costume is a mouse with big ears.

What is her costume?

Molly likes her mouse tail the best.

What does she like best?

She will say "Happy Halloween" when her friend opens the door.

What is Molly going to say?

Language Expansion Activities

1. Molly likes her tail. Can you find it? Can you follow the tail with your finger? Now color it any color you want.

2. Her mouse costume has two ears. Do they look big or little? Count how many ears you see. Now color them the same color.

3. Can you see any of Molly's hair? What is in her hair? Are they part of her costume? What color do you want to color her hair? Color the rest of Molly's costume a different color.

4. Look at Molly. Is she standing up? What is she doing? Can you crawl around like a little mouse? Do you remember what the little mouse said?

Story 9- Halloween Night

Activity 10
Cowboy Bobby

Bobby is dressed up in cowboy clothes.

What kind of clothes is Bobby wearing?

He has a cowboy hat on his head.

What is on his head?

He is going to play a cowboy game.

What is he going to play?

His boots make a "clump-clump" sound when he walks.

How do his boots sound?

Bobby has his hands behind his back.

Where are Bobby's hands?

Language Expansion Activities

1. Bobby likes to play "dress-up." Do you ever get to play "dress-up" games? What do you like to wear? Can you name the different things Bobby is wearing? (vest, hat, shirt)

2. He has special pants over his jeans. They are called "chaps." Point to them and color them brown.

3. What color would you like to make Bobby's hat? Do you remember where it is?

4. He has a vest over his shirt. Color his vest and shirt different colors.

5. What is Bobby wearing on his feet? What color can you make them?

6. Does Bobby have fun being a cowboy? Do you think he will play inside or outside?

Story 10- Cowboy Bobby

Activity 11
Surprise for Mother

Pete has made a present.

What did Pete make?

The present is for his mother.

Who is the present for?

Pete made a big valentine.

Is Pete's valentine big or little?

The valentine will be a surprise for Mother.

What will be a surprise for Mother?

Pete's mother will be so happy.

Will Pete's mother be happy or sad?

Language Expansion Activities

1. Pete is standing up. Is he holding the valentine in front or in back?

2. What color will you make the valentine?

3. Do you think Pete's mother will give him a hug? Why? Have you ever made a valentine?

4. Can you finish coloring Pete's clothes? First, name all the different kinds of clothes you see.

Story 11- Surprise for Mother

Activity 12
A Blue Ribbon for Don

Don lives on a farm.

Where does Don live?

He has a turkey for a pet.

What is his pet?

Every day he gives the turkey food and water.

What does he give the turkey?

Don is taking the turkey to the fair.

Where is he taking the turkey?

If his turkey is the best turkey, Don will win a blue ribbon.

What will he win?

Language Expansion Activities

1. Don's turkey is very big. Do you think Don will win?

2. Have you been to the fair? What can you tell me about the fair?

3. Let's draw a ribbon on Don's shirt. Can you color it blue?

4. Turkeys can be all different shades of brown. Can you use light and dark brown colors to color the turkey's feathers?

5. The turkey has a red wattle hanging near his beak. Can you color it?

6. Does your turkey look like a winner? Why?

Story 12- A Blue Ribbon for Don

Copyright © 1996 by Academic Communication Associates. This page may be reproduced.

29

Activity 13
Paul's New Pet

Paul has a brand new pet penguin.

What does Paul have?

The penguin lives outside in the cold.

Where does the penguin live?

Paul has to put on a jacket and mittens to go outside.

What does Paul have to put on?

He wishes that the penguin could come inside.

Where does Paul wish the penguin could come?

Paul gets very cold when he's outside for a long time.

When does Paul get cold?

Language Expansion Activities

1. Do you think a penguin would be fun to have as a pet? Do you know what color penguins are?

2. The penguin is not all black and white. He has an orange beak and feet. Can you color these spots orange?

3. What is Paul wearing? Can you find his boots? How many do you see? Color them red.

4. What would you name this penguin? Let's write its name on the coloring page.

Story 13- Paul's New Pet

Activity 14
Time for New Glasses

Matt wears glasses.

What does Matt wear?

Matt tripped and fell down today.

What happened to Matt?

Matt's glasses fell off.

What fell off?

The glasses fell onto the hard ground.

Where did the glasses fall?

The glasses broke when they hit the ground.

When did the glasses break?

Now Matt needs new glasses.

What does Matt need now?

Language Expansion Activities

1. Touch the glasses in the picture. Do you wear glasses? Do you know someone who does? Can you color the glasses?

2. Look at Matt's face. Does he look sad or happy? How do you feel when you fall? How do you feel when you break something?

3. Can you remember the last time that you fell? Were you inside or outside? Where do you think Matt is? If he is outside, draw in some grass.

4. Would you like to color the rest of the picture? What needs to be colored?

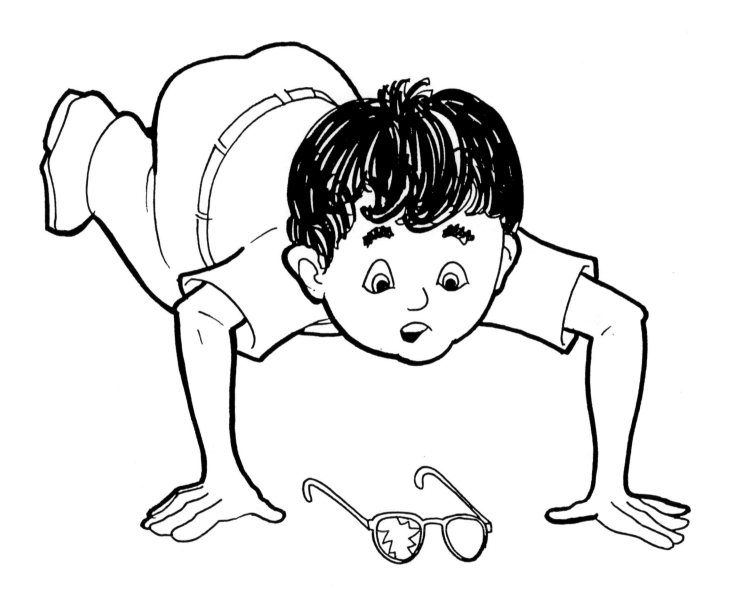

Story 14- Time for New Glasses

Activity 15
Outside Fun

Sue is playing outside.

Where is Sue playing?

She is trying to play tennis.

What is she trying to play?

She needs to hit the ball with the racket.

What is she going to hit with the racket?

The ball is very little and hard to hit.

Is the ball little or big?

Sue hit the ball!

What did Sue hit?

Now she thinks this is a fun game.

Is this a fun game?

Language Expansion Activities

1. Sue is holding a tennis racket. Can you point to it? How many hands is she using to hold the racket?

2. Where is the little ball? Trace the ball with your finger. Is it round or square?

3. Sue is wearing a skirt and a shirt. Do you think it is cold or hot outside? Color her clothes. What color(s) did you use?

4. The racket is made out of wood. Can you color it brown? Color her hair the same color. What color did you make her hair?

5. Does this look like an inside or outside game? What else do you play outside? Name something that you play inside.

Story 15- Outside Fun

Activity 16
Playing the Drum

David has a new drum.

What does David have?

He sits down to play because the drum is heavy.

Why does he sit down to play?

The sound of the drum can be loud or soft.

How does the drum sound?

David hits the drum with a little stick.

What does he use to hit the drum?

David likes playing the drum while he listens to music.

What does David listen to while playing his drum?

David is happy when he plays his drum.

Is David happy or sad when he plays the drum?

Language Expansion Activities

1. David's drum is special. Can you name something you have that's special?
   Color David's drum a special color. What color did you pick?

2. Can you color David's hair red? He looks very happy. Do you think he is sing-
   ing? Can you sing a song?

3. Where is David sitting? Look around your room. Do you see a chair in the
   room? Color David's chair the same color. What color is it?

4. Is there something that you can use as a drum? Can you beat your drum?
   Make the drum sound loud. Now make it sound soft. What did you use for
   your drum?

Story 16- Playing the Drum

Activity 17
Shopping for Candy

Debbie went shopping with her mom.

What did Debbie do with her mom?

Her mom bought candy.

What did her mom buy?

This is a candy cane.

What kind of candy is this?

She gave one candy cane to Debbie.

How many candy canes did she give to Debbie?

Debbie is going to suck the candy cane.

How will Debbie eat the candy cane?

It will take Debbie a long time to eat the candy.

Will it take Debbie a long or short time to eat the candy?

Language Expansion Activities

1. Candy canes are a fun candy to eat. They smell very good. What do you use to smell the candy cane?

2. You suck a candy cane. What other sweets do you suck or lick? (sucker, ice cream)

3. Can you trace the candy cane with your finger? What color would you like to make it?

4. Debbie is wearing a dress in Christmas colors. Christmas colors are red and green. What colors should Debbie's dress be?

Story 17- Shopping for Candy

Activity 18
Jimmy's New Sailboat

Jimmy has a new sailboat.

What does Jimmy have?

He wants to play with the boat outside.

Where does he want to play with the boat?

It is a nice warm day.

Is the day warm or cold?

Jimmy puts his boat in the little pond.

Where does Jimmy put the boat?

A pond has water in it.

What does a pond have in it?

The boat will float in the pond.

Where will the boat float?

Language Expansion Activities

1. Look at Jimmy's hands. Can you find them both?

2. Is he touching something with one hand? What?

3. Can you color the sail? What color did you use?

4. The boat is floating in a pond. It may float away from Jimmy. Draw a string from the boat to Jimmy's hand. If the boat floats too far away, Jimmy can pull it back with the string.

5. It is a warm day. What is Jimmy wearing?

6. Don't forget to look at his feet. What do you call the shoes that he is wearing?

7. Color Jimmy's clothes to match your clothes.

Story 18- Jimmy's New Sailboat

Activity 19
Watch Me Build

Scotty is playing with blocks.

What is Scotty playing with?

"Watch me build," says Scotty.

What does Scotty say?

Scotty builds with three blocks.

How many blocks does he have?

He puts one block on top of another block.

What does he put on top?

He makes a block tower.

What does he make with the blocks?

"Boom!" says Scotty when he knocks the blocks down.

What does Scotty say when he knocks the blocks down?

Language Expansion Activities

1. Scotty is playing with blocks. Can you point to the block in his hand? On the floor? How many blocks do you see? Color the blocks all the same color. What color did you use?

2. Scotty built a tower with his blocks. Can you name something else that you can build with blocks?

3. Color Scotty's clothes using different colors. What color did you make his shirt? What color did you make his pants? Did you color both shoes the same color or a different color?

Story 19- Watch Me Build

Activity 20
Quiet Time

It is quiet time for Sarah.

What time is it for Sarah?

She likes to read during her quiet time.

What does she like to do?

She is reading a big book today.

Is she reading a big book or a little book?

Sarah cannot read the words.

Can she read the words?

She likes to look at the pictures.

What does she do with the pictures?

Her mother will read the story to her later.

When will Sarah's mother read the story?

Language Expansion Activities

1. What is in the picture on the book? This book is about the Three Little Pigs. One pig uses straw to build his house. Another uses sticks to build his house. The last builds his house with bricks. Which pig is in the picture?

2. Look at the house on the book. Is it made of sticks, straw, or bricks?

3. Do you know the story? What does the big bad wolf say?

4. The house on the book is made from straw. Straw is yellow. Can you color the house yellow?

5. What color are you wearing today? Make Sarah's pants and shirt the same color?

6. Is quiet time noisy? What do you do for quiet time at your house? Do you like to be quiet or noisy?

Story 20- Quiet Time

Activity 21
Flowers for Mommy

Ann is picking flowers.

What is Ann picking?

She will give them to her mommy.

Who is she giving the flowers to?

The flowers smell pretty.

How do the flowers smell?

She picked five flowers.

How many flowers did she pick?

Her mommy will say, "Thank you."

What will her mommy say?

Tomorrow, Ann will pick flowers for her daddy.

What will Ann do tomorrow?

Language Expansion Activities

1. Where is Ann? Is she inside or outside?

2. Do you have flowers in your yard? Do you get to pick them?

3. Count the flowers that Ann is holding. How many does she have in one hand? How many are in the other hand?

4. Are there more flowers to pick or did Ann pick them all? Color each flower a different color.

5. What is on her knee? What do you think happened?

6. Ann is wearing a dress. What color would you like to make the dress?

7. What color should the grass be? Color the grass.

Story 21- Flowers for Mommy

Activity 22
Winter Play

Steven looked outside.

Where did Steven look?

He saw snow all over the front yard.

What did he see?

Steven loves to play outside in the snow.

Does Steven love to play in the snow or water?

He put a hat on his head.

Where did he put the hat?

Then he pulled on his two boots.

How many boots did he put on?

Steven is ready to go outside.

Where will Steven go?

Language Expansion Activities

1. Steven is wearing a sweater, hat, boots, and mittens. Do you think it is cold or hot outside? What do the mittens cover? How many does he have?

2. Steven looks like he's having a good time. What did he make with the snow? Is the snowman tall or short?

3. Look at Steven's feet. He is on his toes. What is he trying to do?

3. The snowman has a carrot nose. What color should it be?

4. Make Steven's hat and the snowman's hat the same color.

5. The snowman is wearing something around his neck. Do you know what it is called? Color the scarf the same color as Steven's boots. What color did you use?

Story 22- Winter Play

Activity 23
Up, Down, Around

Amy is on a swing.

Where is Amy?

Amy holds onto the swing's rope.

What does Amy hold?

She likes to make the swing go up and down.

What does she like to do with the swing?

Best of all, Amy likes it when the swing goes around and around.

What does Amy like best?

Amy is happy when she swings.

Is Amy happy or sad?

Language Expansion Activities

1. Do you think Amy is swinging outside or inside? Where do you think the swing is? (backyard, park, etc.)

2. Can you name two things that you see in places that have swings? (slide, pool, etc.)

3. Amy has bows in her hair. How many bows do you see? Color them the same color. Color her hair a different color.

4. Are you wearing a shirt today? What color is it? Color Amy's shirt the same color as yours.

Story 23- Up, Down, Around

Activity 24
Ice Cream Treat

Mommy gave Tommy an ice cream cone.

What did Mommy give Tommy?

He was so happy!

Was Tommy happy or sad?

Uh-oh! The ice cream fell off the cone!

What fell?

Before Tommy could catch it, the ice cream fell on the ground.

Where did the ice cream fall?

Now Tommy is feeling sad.

How is Tommy feeling without the ice cream?

Language Expansion Activities

1. Do you think Mommy will make another cone for him?

2. Tommy loves ice cream. Is ice cream cold or hot?

3. Tommy had two scoops of ice cream. Make one scoop chocolate by coloring it brown. Can you make a strawberry scoop using a pink crayon?

4. Point to Tommy's shirt. What color do you want to color it?

5. Point to his pants. Can you color his pants a different color?

6. Tommy looks sad. What do you see on his face that lets you know he is sad?

Story 24- Ice Cream Treat

Activity 25
The Little Puppy

Sally is holding a little puppy.

What is Sally holding?

She is holding it in her arms.

Where is the puppy?

The puppy is wiggling.

What is the puppy doing?

It is hard for Sally to hold the puppy.

Is it hard or easy to hold the puppy?

The puppy licks Sally's chin.

What does the puppy lick?

The puppy's tongue tickles Sally.

What tickles Sally?

Language Expansion Activities

1. Look at the picture. Which one is big, Sally or the puppy? Which one is little?

2. The puppy is wiggling his body. Can you wiggle around? Is it hard for your mommy or daddy to hold you when you wiggle?

3. Many puppies are white, brown, or black. Which of these colors would you like to make Sally's puppy? Are you going to use one color or two?

3. What color is your hair? Color Sally's hair the same color.

4. What did the puppy do to tickle Sally's chin?

Story 25- The Little Puppy

Activity 26
Learning to Dance

Carrie is learning to dance.

What is Carrie learning to do?

She is wearing special dance shoes.

What is she wearing?

She will learn to spin around.

Will she learn to spin?

Carrie must listen to the music.

What will Carrie listen to?

She will dance when she hears the music.

When will she dance?

When the music stops, she will stop dancing.

What happens when the music stops?

Language Expansion Activities

1. Carrie is learning a dance called ballet. She will learn to jump and turn to the music. Can you dance to music? Can you listen and stop when the music stops? Show us how you would dance.

2. Carrie is wearing a special dance outfit. It is called a tutu. It has a pretty ruffle all around the bottom. Can you color it?

3. Her shoes are special, too. They are called ballet slippers. Color them the same color as the tutu. Do you have slippers? Do they look the same as Carrie's slippers?

Story 26- Learning to Dance

Activity 27
Taking a Trip

Linda is going on a trip.

Where is Linda going?

She has two suitcases.

How many suitcases does she have?

Linda put all her clothes in the big suitcase.

Where did Linda put her clothes?

She put her books and toys in the little suitcase.

What did she put in the little suitcase?

She is holding a ticket.

What is she holding?

Linda is going to visit her grandma.

Who is Linda going to visit?

Language Expansion Activities

1. Have you ever gone on a trip? Where did you go? Who went with you?

2. Linda is going to go on an airplane. Have you been on an airplane? Tell me about it.

3. Where is the ticket? Color the ticket red.

4. Count the suitcases. Touch the big suitcase. Now touch the little suitcase. Color one suitcase brown. Color one suitcase blue. Which one did you color brown? Which one did you color blue?

5. What would you put in the suitcase? Name two toys that you would put in the little suitcase? Name two kinds of clothes that you would put in the big one.

6. Does Linda look happy or sad? Do you think she will have a good time?

Story 27- Taking a Trip

Activity 28
Out for a Walk

Jeff is going outside for a walk.

Where is Jeff going?

It is cold outside.

Is it cold or hot?

Jeff is wearing his heavy coat.

What is he wearing?

His mittens will help keep his hands warm.

What will his mittens keep warm?

He is wearing boots to keep his feet dry.

What is he wearing to keep his feet dry?

Jeff wants to play with his friend, Tommy.

Who does Jeff want to play with?

Jeff will walk to Tommy's house and ask him to play.

Where will Jeff walk?

Language Expansion Activities

1. Jeff is going outside on a winter day. He is wearing his very warm coat and a hat. What do you wear on a cold day? Do you think Jeff and Tommy will go swimming or play in the snow? Color Jeff's hat and coat the same color?

2. How is Jeff getting to Tommy's house? Where can you go if you take a walk? Where can you go if you ride in a car?

3. Do you remember what Jeff has on his feet? Do you have boots? What kind of shoes are you wearing? Pick a color for Jeff's boots. What color is it?

Story 28- Out for a Walk

Activity 29
Beth Makes a New Friend

Beth has found a new friend.

What did Beth find?

Her friend is a little bunny.

Is her friend a bunny or a cat?

Loud noises scare the bunny.

What scares the bunny?

Beth must be very quiet when she goes up to the bunny.

Should Beth be noisy or quiet near the bunny?

Beth is giving a carrot to the bunny.

What is Beth giving to the bunny?

The bunny hops up next to Beth.

Where does the bunny hop?

Now Beth can pet the bunny.

What can Beth do now?

Language Expansion Activities

1. Bunnies can be many colors. Pick one and color Beth's bunny.

2. What color should the carrot be? Color it. Where do you keep carrots at you house? In the refrigerator?

3. Is Beth's hair long or short? It is tied back with a pretty bow. Touch the bow.

4. Look at the bunny's ears. Are they long or short? Is the tail big or little?

5. What else is Beth wearing?

Story 29- Beth Makes a New Friend

Activity 30
Cindy Bakes Cookies

Cindy is helping her mommy bake.

Who is Cindy helping?

She is making cookies.

What is she making?

The cookies look like gingerbread men.

What do the cookies look like?

The cookies need to be baked in the oven.

Where do the cookies need to be baked?

Cindy wants to eat one of the cookies.

What does Cindy want to do with one of the cookies?

The cookies are too hot.

Are the cookies hot or cold?

Cindy will have to wait.

Why does Cindy have to wait?

Language Expansion Activities

1. Cindy made gingerbread cookies. When they are cool, she can give each one a face. What does she need to put on each face?

2. Gingerbread cookies are brown after they are baked. Color each cookie brown.

3. Cindy is holding the cookie pan with potholders. Point to the potholders. Why does she need potholders? Do you have potholders in the kitchen at home? What do they look like? What color will you make Cindy's potholders? How many do you need to color?

Story 30- Cindy Bakes Cookies

Reproducible
Response Forms

Student:_____ Date:_____

Response Form for Activity 1
Birthday Balloons

Danny is blowing up balloons.

The balloons are for a party.

It is Danny's birthday.

Danny will give a balloon to each of his friends.

1. What is Danny doing?

2. What are the balloons for?

3. Whose birthday is it?

4. What will Danny do with the balloons?

Child's story:

Response Form for Activity 2
Mary's Picnic

Mary is going on a picnic.

She is carrying a heavy basket.

The basket is full of food.

Mary will eat the food for lunch.

1. Where is Mary going?

2. What is heavy?

3. What is in the basket?

4. Who will eat the food?

Child's story:

Response Form for Activity 3
Going Fishing

Johnny is going fishing.

He is carrying a pole in one hand.

He is holding a worm in the other hand.

Johnny fishes at a pond.

1. Where is Johnny going?

2. What is Johnny carrying?

3. What is in his other hand?

4. Where does Johnny fish?

Child's story:

Response Form for Activity 4
Take My Picture

Polly has a new camera.

She is taking pictures.

She wants to take your picture.

She will tell you, "Smile."

1. What does Polly have?

2. What is Polly doing with the camera?

3. Whose picture does she want to take?

4. What will she tell you?

Child's story:

Response Form for Activity 5
Let's Play Ball

Ben is playing baseball.

Baseball is his favorite game.

He is wearing a glove on one hand.

Ben is holding his glove up.

He will catch the ball with the glove.

1. What is Ben doing?

2. What is his favorite game?

3. Where is the glove?

4. Is he holding the glove up or down?

5. What will he do with the glove?

Child's story:

Response Form for Activity 6
A Special Toy

Katie is holding a toy bunny.

Katie loves her bunny.

The bunny's name is Floppy.

Floppy sleeps with Katie at night.

1. What is she holding?

2. Does Katie love her bunny?

3. What is the bunny's name?

4. Who sleeps with Floppy?

Child's story:

Response Form for Activity 7
Butterflies

Andy is standing very still.

He is watching the butterflies.

The butterflies are flying around Andy.

When Andy moves, the butterflies will fly away.

Andy will try to catch the butterflies in his net.

1. Is Andy standing or sitting?

2. What is he watching?

3. Where are the butterflies flying?

4. What will happen when Andy moves?

5. What will Andy try to catch in his net?

Child's story:

Response Form for Activity 8
Work of Art

Jill likes to paint.

She is holding her paint brush.

She is painting on the paper.

She painted a picture of one house.

She is going to give the picture to her mom.

1. What does Jill like to do?

2. What is she holding in her hand?

3. Where is she painting?

4. How many pictures did she paint?

5. Who is she going to give the picture to?

Child's story:

Response Form for Activity 9
Halloween Night

Molly is going to her friend's party on Halloween.

She is dressed in her Halloween costume.

Her costume is a mouse with big ears.

Molly likes her mouse tail the best.

She will say "Happy Halloween" when her friend opens the door.

1. Where is Molly going?

2. What is she wearing?

3. What is her costume?

4. What does she like best?

5. What is Molly going to say?

Child's story:

Response Form for Activity 10
Cowboy Bobby

Bobby is dressed up in cowboy clothes.

He has a cowboy hat on his head.

He is going to play a cowboy game.

His boots make a "clump-clump" sound when he walks.

Bobby has his hands behind his back.

1. What kind of clothes is Bobby wearing?

2. What is on his head?

3. What is he going to play?

4. How do his boots sound?

5. Where are Bobby's hands?

Child's story:

Response Form for Activity 11
Surprise For Mother

Pete has made a present.

The present is for his mother.

Pete made a big valentine.

The valentine will be a surprise for Mother.

Pete's mother will be so happy.

1. What did Pete make?

2. Who is the present for?

3. Is Pete's valentine big or little?

4. What will be a surprise for Mother?

5. Will Pete's mother be happy or sad?

Child's story:

Response Form for Activity 12
A Blue Ribbon For Don

Don lives on a farm.

He has a turkey for a pet.

Every day he gives the turkey food and water.

Don is taking the turkey to the fair.

If his turkey is the best turkey, Don will win a blue ribbon.

1. Where does Don live?

2. What is his pet?

3. What does he give the turkey?

4. Where is he taking the turkey?

5. What will he win?

Child's story:

Response Form for Activity 13
Paul's New Pet

Paul has a brand new pet penguin.

The penguin lives outside in the cold.

Paul has to put on a jacket and mittens to go outside.

He wishes that the penguin could come inside.

Paul gets very cold when he's outside for a long time.

1. What does Paul have?

2. Where does the penguin live?

3. What does Paul have to put on?

4. Where does Paul wish the penguin could come?

5. When does Paul get cold?

Child's story:

Response Form for Activity 14
Time For New Glasses

Matt wears glasses.

Matt tripped and fell down today.

Matt's glasses fell off.

The glasses fell onto the hard ground.

The glasses broke when they hit the ground.

Now Matt needs new glasses.

1. What does Matt wear?

2. What happened to Matt?

3. What fell off?

4. Where did the glasses fall?

5. When did the glasses break?

6. What does Matt need now?

Child's story:

Response Form for Activity 15
Outside Fun

Sue is playing outside.

She is trying to play tennis.

She needs to hit the ball with the racket.

The ball is very little and hard to hit.

Sue hit the ball!

Now she thinks this is a fun game.

1. Where is Sue playing?

2. What is she trying to play?

3. What is she going to hit with the racket?

4. Is the ball little or big?

5. What did Sue hit?

6. Is this a fun game?

Child's story:

Response Form for Activity 16
Playing the Drum

David has a new drum.

He sits down to play because the drum is heavy.

The sound of the drum can be loud or soft.

David hits the drum with a little stick.

David likes playing the drum while he listens to music.

David is happy when he plays his drum.

1. What does David have?

2. Why does he sit down to play?

3. How does the drum sound?

4. What does he use to hit the drum?

5. What does David listen to while playing his drum?

6. Is David happy or sad when he plays the drum?

Child's story:

Record for for Activity 17
Shopping For Candy

Debbie went shopping with her mom.

Her mom bought candy.

This is a candy cane.

She gave one candy cane to Debbie.

Debbie is going to suck the candy cane.

It will take Debbie a long time to eat the candy.

1. What did Debbie do with her mom?

2. What did her mom buy?

3. What kind of candy is this?

4. How many candy canes did she give to Debbie?

5. How will Debbie eat the candy cane?

6. Will it take Debbie a long time or a short time to eat the candy?

Child's story:

Response Form for Activity 18
Jimmy's New Sailboat

Jimmy has a new sailboat.

He wants to play with the boat outside.

It is a nice warm day.

Jimmy puts his boat in the little pond.

A pond has water in it.

The boat will float in the pond.

1. What does Jimmy have?

2. Where does he want to play with the boat?

3. Is the day warm or cold?

4. Where does Jimmy put the boat?

5. What does a pond have in it?

6. Where will the boat float?

Child's story:

Response Form for Activity 19
Watch Me Build

Scotty is playing with blocks.

"Watch me build," says Scotty.

Scotty builds with three blocks.

He puts one block on top of another block.

He makes a block tower.

"Boom!" says Scotty when he knocks the blocks down.

1. What is Scotty playing with?

2. What does Scotty say?

3. How many blocks does he have?

4. What does he put on top?

5. What does he make with the blocks?

6. What does Scotty say when he knocks the blocks down?

Child's story:

Response Form for Activity 20
Quiet Time

It is quiet time for Sarah.

She likes to read during her quiet time.

She is reading a big book today.

Sarah cannot read the words.

She likes to look at the pictures.

Her mother will read the story to her later.

1. What time is it for Sarah?

2. What does she like to do?

3. Is she reading a big book or a little book?

4. Can she read the words?

5. What does she do with the pictures?

6. When will Sarah's mother read the story?

Child's story:

Response Form for Activity 21
Flowers for Mommy

Ann is picking flowers.

She will give them to her mommy.

The flowers smell pretty.

She picked five flowers.

Her mommy will say, "Thank you."

Tomorrow, Ann will pick flowers for her daddy.

1. What is Ann picking?

2. Who is she giving the flowers to?

3. How do the flowers smell?

4. How many flowers did she pick?

5. What will her mommy say?

6. What will Ann do tomorrow?

Child's story:

Response Form for Activity 22
Winter Play

Steven looked outside.

He saw snow all over the front yard.

Steven loves to play outside in the snow.

He put a hat on his head.

Then he pulled on his two boots.

Steven is ready to go outside.

1. Where did Steven look?

2. What did he see?

3. Does Steven love to play in the snow or water?

4. Where did he put the hat?

5. How many boots did he put on?

6. Where will Steven go?

Child's story:

Response Form for Activity 23
Up, Down, Around

Amy is on a swing.

Amy holds onto the swing's rope.

She likes to make the swing go up and down.

Best of all, Amy likes it when the swing goes around and around.

Amy is happy when she swings.

1. Where is Amy?

2. What does Amy hold?

3. What does she like to do with the swing?

4. What does Amy like best?

5. Is Amy happy or sad?

Child's story:

Response Form for Activity 24
Ice Cream Treat

Mommy gave Tommy an ice cream cone.

He was so happy!

Uh-oh! The ice cream fell off the cone!

Before Tommy could catch it, the ice cream fell on the ground.

Now Tommy is feeling sad.

1. What did Mommy give Tommy?

2. Was Tommy happy or sad?

3. What fell?

4. Where did the ice cream fall?

5. How is Tommy feeling without the ice cream?

Child's story:

Response Form for Activity 25
The Little Puppy

Sally is holding a little puppy.

She is holding it in her arms.

The puppy is wiggling.

It is hard for Sally to hold the puppy.

The puppy licks Sally's chin.

The puppy's tongue tickles Sally.

1. What is Sally holding?

2. Where is the puppy?

3. What is the puppy doing?

4. Is it hard or easy to hold the puppy?

5. What does the puppy lick?

6. What tickles Sally?

Child's story:

Response Form for Activity 26
Learning to Dance

Carrie is learning to dance.

She is wearing special dance shoes.

She will learn to spin around.

Carrie must listen to the music.

She will dance when she hears the music.

When the music stops, she will stop dancing.

1. What is Carrie learning to do?

2. What is she wearing?

3. Will she learn to spin?

4. What will Carrie listen to?

5. When will she dance?

6. What happens when the music stops?

Child's story:

Response Form for Activity 27
Taking a Trip

Linda is going on a trip.

She has two suitcases.

Linda put all her clothes in the big suitcase.

She put her books and toys in the little suitcase.

She is holding a ticket.

Linda is going to visit her grandma.

1. Where is Linda going?

2. How many suitcases does she have?

3. Where did Linda put her clothes?

4. What did she put in the little suitcase?

5. What is she holding?

6. Who is Linda going to visit?

Child's story:

Response Form for Activity 28
Out for a Walk

Jeff is going outside for a walk.

It is cold outside.

Jeff is wearing his heavy coat.

His mittens will help keep his hands warm.

He is wearing boots to keep his feet dry.

Jeff wants to play with his friend, Tommy.

Jeff will walk to Tommy's house and ask him to play.

1. Where is Jeff going?

2. Is it cold or hot?

3. What is he wearing?

4. What will his mittens keep warm?

5. What is he wearing to keep his feet dry?

6. Who does Jeff want to play with?

7. Where will Jeff walk?

Child's story:

Response Form for Activity 29
Beth Makes a New Friend

Beth has found a new friend.

Her friend is a little bunny.

Loud noises scare the bunny.

Beth must be very quiet when she goes up to the bunny.

Beth is giving a carrot to the bunny.

The bunny hops up next to Beth.

Now Beth can pet the bunny.

1. What did Beth find?

2. Is her friend a bunny or a cat?

3. What scares the bunny?

4. Should Beth be noisy or quiet near the bunny?

5. What is Beth giving to the bunny?

6. Where does the bunny hop?

7. What can Beth do now?

Child's story:

Response Form for Activity 30
Cindy Bakes Cookies

Cindy is helping her mommy bake.

She is making cookies.

The cookies look like gingerbread men.

The cookies need to be baked in the oven.

Cindy wants to eat one of the cookies.

The cookies are too hot.

Cindy will have to wait.

1. Who is Cindy helping?

2. What is she making?

3. What do the cookies look like?

4. Where do the cookies need to be baked?

5. What does Cindy want to do with one of the cookies?

6. Are the cookies hot or cold?

7. Why does Cindy have to wait?

Child's story: